Poems
from the
Sac Magique

Lots ti

Poems
from the
Sac Magique

Written by Jack Ousbey
Illustrated by Penny Lane

A Ragdoll Production for
Central Independent Television

Hippo

For Jenny, Emma and Gran

Scholastic Children's Books,
Scholastic Publications Ltd,
7-9 Pratt Street, London NW1 OAE, UK

Scholastic Inc.,
555 Broadway, New York, NY 10012-3999, USA

Scholastic Canada Ltd,
123 Newkirk Road, Richmond Hill,
Ontario, Canada L4C 3G5

Ashton Scholastic Pty Ltd,
P O Box 579, Gosford, New South Wales,
Australia

Ashton Scholastic Ltd,
Private Bag 92801, Penrose, Auckland,
New Zealand

Published by Scholastic Children's Books, 1994

Text copyright © Jack Ousbey, 1994
Illustrations copyright © Penny Lane, 1994

Design of Tots - TV puppets and house
copyright © Ragdoll Productions (UK) Ltd, 1993
Central logo copyright © Central Independent Television plc, 1989
Based on the Central Independent Television series produced by
Ragdoll Productions

ISBN 0 590 55740 8

Typeset by Rapid Reprographics
Printed by Cox & Wyman Ltd, Reading, Berkshire.

Contents

Introduction

There is now a lot of evidence to show that children whose parents read to them regularly are more likely to become good readers themselves. The act of sharing stories and poems enables the young child to make sense of a whole range of language forms, and to begin to understand how words are used in different contexts.

Poems and rhymes are particularly important at this stage. The young listener finds out, almost effortlessly, about the music and rhythms of language and how words sound "inside the head". Building up a store of information concerning books and book language, rhymes, sounds and word-order, is an excellent way of preparing to be a reader. Children whose parents provide them with such experiences have an enormous advantage over those who never encounter poems and stories in their formative years.

Poems from the Sac Magique is designed as a reading experience to accompany the Tots TV series. Young children, and fans of the Tots and their adventures will enjoy finding out more about them in this book. And, because the poems are written to be read aloud, as a shared event, they will be keen to join in with those words and phrases they enjoy and remember. This is how a good reader begins, as a willing partner with an adult who is prepared to spend time on this worthwhile activity.

Jack Ousbey

Sac Magique

This is the house
Where the Tots live.

This is the door,
At the front of the house,
Where the Tots live.

This is the peg,
Behind the door,
At the front of the house,
Where the Tots live.

This is the bag,
That hangs on the peg,
Behind the door,
At the front of the house,
Where the Tots live.

AND IN THAT BAG,
YOU MAY FIND...

A whistle to blow, a silver ring,
A kite to fly, a piece of string.
A large green apple, a small brown seed,
And lots of magic poems to read...

Breakfast

Tiny likes breakfasts
That crackle and pop.
Tilly likes cornflakes,
  With sugar on top.
  Tom likes honey,
  Spread on his toast.
What kind of breakfast
  Do you like most?

Our House

We are the Tots,
And this is our house.
We like living here,
And adventuring out.

In town, at the zoo,
On the beach, in the street.
We like having fun,
With the people we meet.

We play well together,
Sometimes alone.
We always feel safe,
In our own little home.

We are the Tots,
And this is our house.
We like living here,
And adventuring out.

Who?

Who is good at bouncing and swinging?
Tiny.
Who is good at painting and singing?
Tilly.
And who is the Tot who knows a lot?
Tom. Tom. Tom.

Who is good at tricking and teasing?
Tiny.
Who is good at hugging and squeezing?
Tilly.
And who is the Tot who knows a lot?
Tom. Tom. Tom.

Busy

Tiny's in the kitchen,
Washing up the pots.
Tom is painting pictures,
With lots of dabs and dots.
Tilly's in the window seat,
Donkey's in the stable.
And Furryboo is peeping out,
From underneath the table.

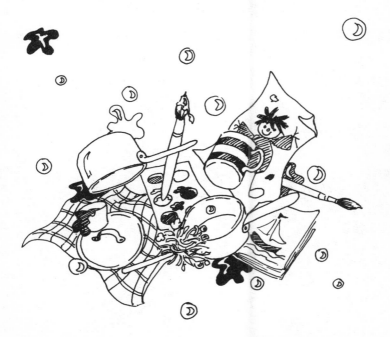

Window Cleaning

Wet cloth and squeeze,
Whistle and shine.
No one has windows
Cleaner than mine.

Cloth in the water,
Squeeze it out tight.
Up and down, sideways,
Shiny and bright.

This window is clean,
This window is shiny.
This window's the best,
And my name is Tiny.

Lonely

I haven't any friends, Donkey,
I'm all on my own.
I'm feeling really sad, Donkey,
I don't like being alone.

I need a little hug, Donkey,
I need someone who's kind.
I'd like you as a friend, Donkey,
If you don't mind.

Tickling Tots

If Tilly tickles Tiny,
Whilst Tiny tickles Tom,
And Tom decides to tickle Tilly,
What is going on?

Banana Tot

Tots, do you love me?
Yes, quite a lot.
Then why do you call me
Banana Tot?

It's not that we're cross,
We're certain we're not.
It's just that you are...well,
A Banana Tot!

Donkey

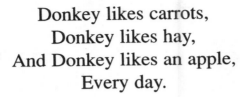

Donkey likes carrots,
Donkey likes hay,
And Donkey likes an apple,
Every day.

Eat up, Donkey,
Carrots and hay.
Here is your apple,
Now what do you say?

EEE AWW!

What I Care About...

"What I care about," says Tom,
"Is keeping the home tidy and clean.
That's what I care about,
Know what I mean?"

"What I care about," says Tilly,
"Is having a hug, like this.
That's what I care about,
Oh, and a kiss."

"What I care about," says Tiny,
"Is cooking good things to eat.
That's what I care about,
A real treat."

Hullabaloo

Listen to the noise when the Tots play trains,
With a clatter-bang, huff-puff-chuff.
Oh, what a din when they all run in,
With their box of dressing-up stuff.
My, what a fuss when Tiny dresses up,
In a long, red gown and a hat.
And Tilly says it's time for a new kind of game,
With a big blue ball and a bat.
And Tiny swings and Tilly skips,
And Tom stands on his head.
Then they give three cheers as they run upstairs,
And bounce on Tilly's bed.

What a noise, what a fuss, what a ding-dong-do.
What a clatter-bang-crash, what a hullabaloo.
What a nattering, chattering kind of day,
When the Tots decide it's time for play.

Watching

We're watching a goat,
We're touching her coat,
We're stroking her ears and her nose.
When, skippety, hoppety, hoofs in-the-air,
She hoppety, skippety goes.

Clop-clop, swing along,
Swish-a-tail, neigh.
Horse in the meadow
Is up and away.
Frolicking and frisking,
As if to say,
It's a kick-a-leg, shake-a-mane,
Swish-a-tail day.

Chip-a-bit, tap-a-bit,
Tots are watching.
Push-a-bit, out-a-bit,
Little chick hatching.

Just watch a puppy, a black and white romper.
A bustler, a bouncer, a champion jumper.
A racer, a chaser, a never-still boy,
A happy-to-be-here, bundle of joy.
A wag-a-tail fellow who seems to be saying
It's great being a puppy, all barking and playing.

Painting, Playing and Reading

When Tiny is painting,
Tiny likes pictures.
With all kinds of colours,
And all sorts of mixtures.
With tigers and parrots,
And rainbows and lightning.
Giants and monsters,
And things that are frightening.
That's what Tiny likes.

When she's playing her flute,
Tilly likes tunes,
That hang in the air
Like blown-up balloons,
Then suddenly burst
Into flowers of sound,
And quietly, slowly,
Come back to the ground.
That's what Tilly likes.

When Tom is reading,
He's not here it seems.
He's filling his head
With his story-world dreams.
Jugglers and jesters,
Wizards and kings,
Pirates and treasure,
Dragons with wings.
That's what Tom likes.

Tots Skipping

Swing-skip
Swing-skip
One, two
Three, four

Swing-hop
Swing-hop
Swing-skip
Swing-hop

Swing rope
Swing rope

Swing-g-g
Swing-g-g

Swing-skip
Swing-skip
One, two
Three, four

Faster
Faster
Faster
Faster

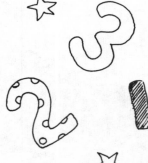

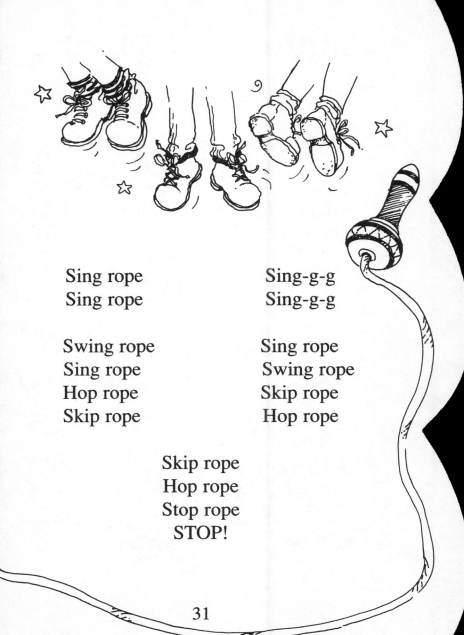

Sing rope
Sing rope

Sing-g-g
Sing-g-g

Swing rope
Sing rope
Hop rope
Skip rope

Sing rope
Swing rope
Skip rope
Hop rope

Skip rope
Hop rope
Stop rope
STOP!

Squeaky Squeak

Mouse, mouse,
Loose in our house.
Mind your toes!
There he goes!
With a squeak, squeaky, squeak,
And a twitch of his whiskery nose.

Mouse, mouse,
Loose in our house.
There! There!
Under the chair!
With a squeak, squeaky, squeak,
And the tip of his tail in the air.

Mouse, mouse,
Are you still in our house?
Somewhere near,
We can hear.
With a squeak, squeaky, squeak,
But we can't see you, mouse, anywhere.

When

Tiny tests the water,
Then puts his feet right in it.
"I think I'll have a bath," he says,
"This minute."

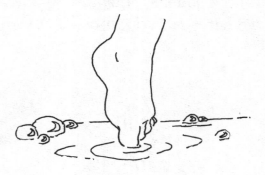

Tom looks in the farmer's field,
And sees a friendly cow.
"Can you jump over the moon," he says,
"Right now?"

Tilly puts her left shoe on,
Then puts on her right.
"My feet are going for a walk," she says,
"Tonight."

A Pudding,
a Kite and a Book

Tiny is working, Tiny is working,
Tiny is baking a pudding.
With – carrots, sultanas,
    Two small bananas,
    A handful of nuts and a plum.
    Apples and cherries,
    A pound of fresh berries,
    And quite a big spoonful of jam.

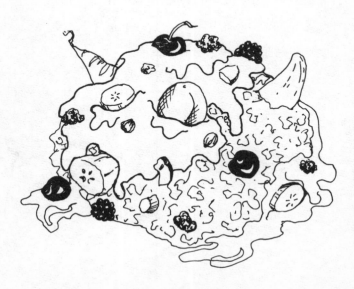

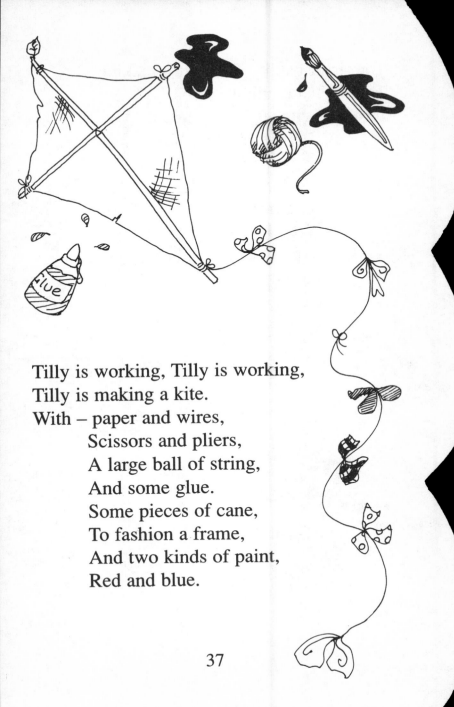

Tilly is working, Tilly is working,
Tilly is making a kite.
With – paper and wires,
       Scissors and pliers,
       A large ball of string,
       And some glue.
       Some pieces of cane,
       To fashion a frame,
       And two kinds of paint,
       Red and blue.

Tom isn't baking, Tom isn't making,
Tom is just reading a book.
About – witches and wizards,
        Rainstorms and blizzards,
        A woodcutter's son,
        And a horse.
        A girl in a dress,
        Who becomes a princess,
        And marries the hero,
        Of course.

Going to the Zoo

Qu'est-ce-qu'on va faire, Tom?
Qu'est-ce-qu'on va faire?
We are going to visit the zoo, Tilly,
We are going to visit the zoo.
Et qu'est-ce-qu'on va voir, Tom?
Qu'est-ce-qu'on va voir?
We are going to watch the animals, Tilly,
Two by two.

Tilly

Je m'appelle Tilly,
Je suis Française.
J'habite à la campagne,
Je ne suis pas Anglaise.

Pains and Pills

Tiny's caught a cold,
He's snuffly and wheezy.
And every so often,
Exceedingly sneezy.
ATISHOO, ATISHOO, ATISHOO!

Tom's got a pain,
He's mumbly and moany.
His tummy is also
Exceedingly groany.
OOOWAH, OOOWAH, OOOWAH!

Tilly, the doctor,
Will cure all their ills.
Now she's going to give them
Some get-well-quick pills.
OUVREZ MES PETITS!

Market Stall

Balloons – balloons – big, blue balloons,
Beachballs – big, bouncy, blue beachballs.
Blue balloons and bouncy beachballs,
Who'll buy – who'll buy?
My blue balloons and bouncy beachballs?

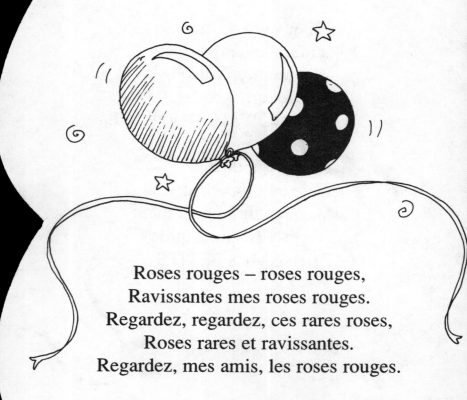

Roses rouges – roses rouges,
Ravissantes mes roses rouges.
Regardez, regardez, ces rares roses,
Roses rares et ravissantes.
Regardez, mes amis, les roses rouges.

Gorgeous green grapes, grown in the greenhouse,
Greenhouse grapes for sale.
Give green grapes as gifts to Grandma.
Graded greenhouse-grown grapes for sale.
The grandest green grapes from the garden.

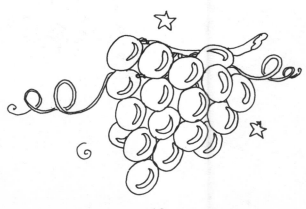

Pretending

Look at Tom, the baker,
As busy as can be.
Flour bin, baking tin,
Mixing bowl and rolling pin.
Look at Tom, the baker,
Making cakes for tea.

Tilly is the doctor,
Ringing on the bell.
Cotton wool, pills and slings,
Stethoscopes, injection things.
Tilly is the doctor,
Making people well.

Tiny is an emperor,
Dressing for the ball.
Silver rings, golden crown,
Shining shoes, scarlet gown.
Tiny is an emperor,
The finest of them all.

Tea-Time

I would like some crusty bread,
I would like some jam.
Je voudrais de la confiture,
Et je voudrais du pain.

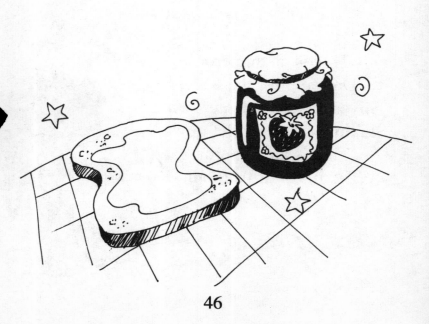

Hugging
and Cuddling

We like playing trains,
All huffing and chugging.
But it's not quite as good
As cuddling and hugging.

We like muddy ground,
For squelching and puddling.
But it's not quite the same
As hugging and cuddling.

Tilly in the Garden

Where are you going, Tilly?
Where are you going today?
Je vais sortir dans le jardin,
Il fait du soleil.

She says she's going in the garden,
It's sunny out there today.
Can we come out as well, Tilly?
D'accord, mes amis, OK.

Looking for Tom

Tiny and Tilly are looking for Tom.
Tom's disappeared, but where has he gone?
Is he under the cart? Or up in the tree?
Or round by the gate? Where can he be?
Tom, Tom, where have you gone?
Tiny and Tilly are looking for Tom.

Can you see where Tom is hiding?

Snow

Soft snow has fallen,
During the night.
The grass snuggles under
A carpet of white.

We climb into our wellies,
Then button up warm.
Make footsteps in circles,
Around the white lawn.

The dresses the trees wear,
Are lacy and white.
We see how they sparkle,
And shine in the night.

Then Tilly comes shouting,
And stomping around.
Clearing a space,
On the cold, frosty ground.

Tom rolls up the snow,
Makes snow-bricks to stack.
We build a white giant,
A snowman called Jack.

My nose-tip has frozen,
Each breath turns to steam.
And the garden is icy,
And still like a dream.

When we look through the window,
Much later at night,
Jack is just standing,
Silent and white.

We wonder, come morning,
Will he still be there?
Alone with the snow,
As it drifts through the air.

Safe Inside

The sky is grey,
The wind is blowing.
The rain is coming,
The light is going.
The night is dark,
The worst of the weather.
But here, inside,
We're safe together.

Reading

Tom is in the window seat,
Just beside the door.
Tilly's on a cushion bed,
Stretched out on the floor.
Tiny's found a special way
To curl up in a chair.
It's reading time inside the house,
And magic's in the air.

Bathtime

We're singing this song from inside the bath,
Where we're playing with ducks and a boat.
We climb in each day, we splash and we play,
And we try things to see if they float.

We don't think the place for washing your face
Is a bath full of bubbles and noise.
We'd rather have fun, once bathtime's begun,
Doing nothing but play with our toys.

Just think a giraffe, when it gets in a bath,
Has to wash straight away, in a rush.
It takes years and years, to wash both its ears,
And scrub down its neck with a brush.

So we're singing away, as we splash and play,
With gurgles and gargles and laughs.
And we're pleased we are Tilly and Tiny and Tom,
And we haven't got necks like giraffes.

57

Hair-Washing Night

Here comes Tilly,
Here comes Tom.
Here comes Tiny,
With his rainhat on.

Tom's big towel
Is fluffy and blue.
Tilly has a bottle
Of yellow shampoo.

Tom has a brush,
Tilly has a comb,
And very special soap,
In the shape of a gnome.

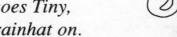

Under goes Tilly,
Under goes Tom.
Under goes Tiny,
With his rainhat on.

58

Scrub-a-rub, one Tot,
Rub-a-dub, two.
Soapsuds flying,
Yellow shampoo.

"Tilly," says Tom,
"Just look at that.
Tiny's hair's still
Under his hat."

Out goes Tilly,
Out goes Tom.
Out goes Tiny,
With his rainhat on.

A Song from the Bookshelf

"Knock, knock," says the Lullaby,
"I'm here to sing."
"I'm waiting," says the Picture Book,
"May I begin?"

"I'm also here," says Alphabet,
"With letters A to Z."
"Look at me," says Story Book,
"I'm waiting to be read."

"Over here," says Fairy Tale,
"I'm next to Nursery Rhyme.
In the land of magic, we call
Once Upon a Time."

Goodnight

We've had some adventures,
Some songs and some fun.
It's time now for sleeping,
Our busy day's done.

So it's Bonne Nuit, Tilly,
And sleep well, Tom.
It's goodnight, Tiny,
And everyone.

61

Sac Magique
Closes

Tilly sleeps,
Tom dreams,
Tiny dozes.
And on its peg,
The sac magique
Closes.

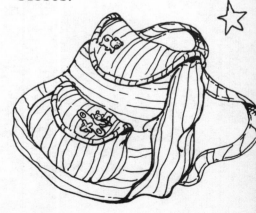

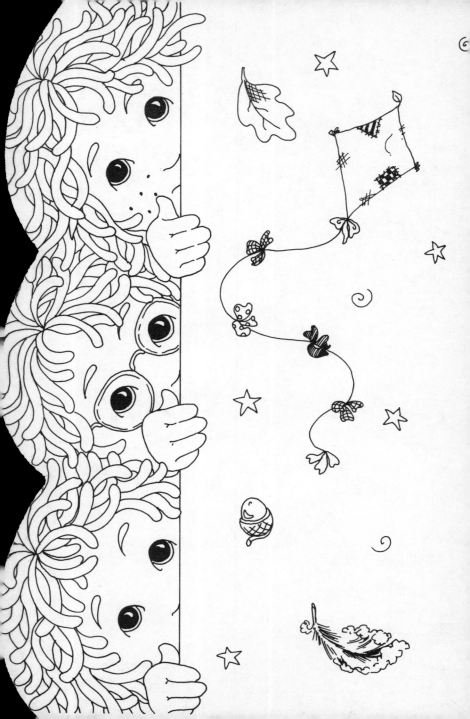